20th ANNIVERSARY

John TRAVOLTA Olivia

GREASE is *still* the word

CONTENTS

PARAMOUNT PICTURES PRESENTS A ROBERT STIGWOOD/ALLAN CARR PRODUCTION JOHN TRAVOLTA OLIVIA NEWTON-JOHN "GREASE" AND STOCKARD CHANNING AS RIZZO WITH SPECIAL GUEST APPEARANCES BY EVE ARDEN, FRANKIE AVALON, JOAN BLONDELL, EDD BYRNES, SID CAESAR, ALICE GHOSTLEY, DODY GOODMAN, SHA-NA-NA SCREENPLAY BY BRONTE WOODARD ADAPTATION BY ALLAN CARR BASED ON THE ORIGINAL MUSICAL BY JIM JACOBS AND WARREN CASEY PRODUCED ON THE BROADWAY STAGE BY KENNETH WAISSMAN AND MAXINE FOX IN ASSOCIATION WITH ANTHONY D'AMATO CHOREOGRAPHY PATRICIA BIRCH

 PG PARENTAL GUIDANCE SUGGESTED SOME MATERIAL MAY NOT BE SUITABLE FOR CHILDREN dts DIGITAL SOUND DOLBY DIGITAL SOUNDTRACK ON POLYDOR CDs AND CASSETTES www.greasemovie.com PRODUCED BY ROBERT STIGWOOD AND ALLAN CARR DIRECTED BY RANDAL KLEISER TM & COPYRIGHT © 1998 BY PARAMOUNT PICTURES. ALL RIGHTS RESERVED

© International Music Publications Ltd

International Music Publications Ltd is a Faber Music company

3 Queen Square, London WC1N 3AU

Printed in England by Caligraving Ltd

All rights reserved

ISBN10: 0-571-53037-0   EAN13: 978-0-571-53037-3

To buy Faber Music publications or to find out about the full range of titles available,
please contact your local music retailer or Faber Music sales enquiries:

Faber Music Ltd, Burnt Mill, Elizabeth Way, Harlow, CM20 2HX England

Tel: +44(0)1279 82 89 82   Fax: +44(0)1279 82 89 83

sales@fabermusic.com   fabermusic.com

GREASE

Words and Music by
BARRY GIBB

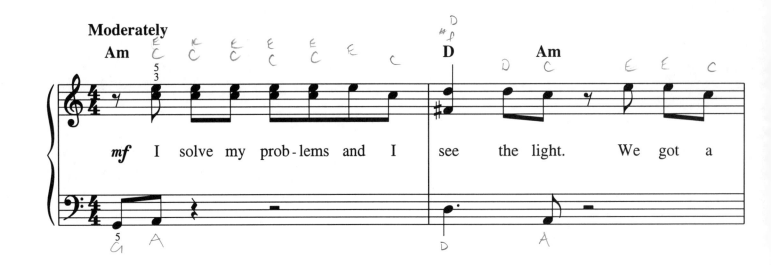

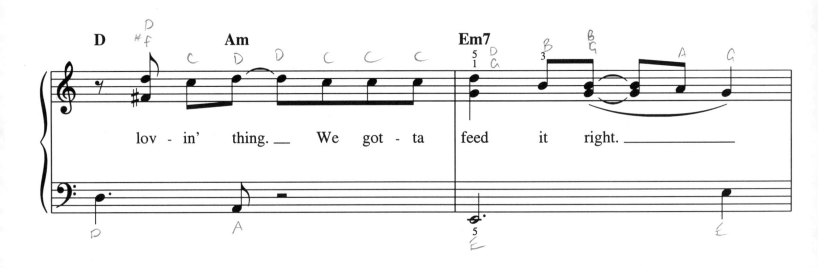

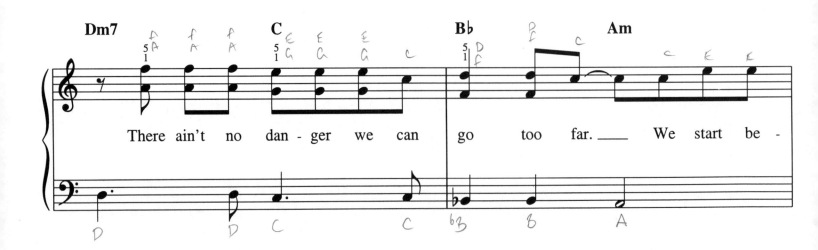

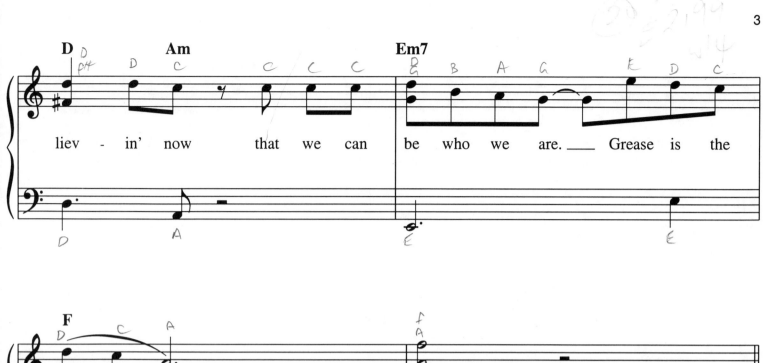

liev - in' now that we can be who we are. ____ Grease is the

word. _____

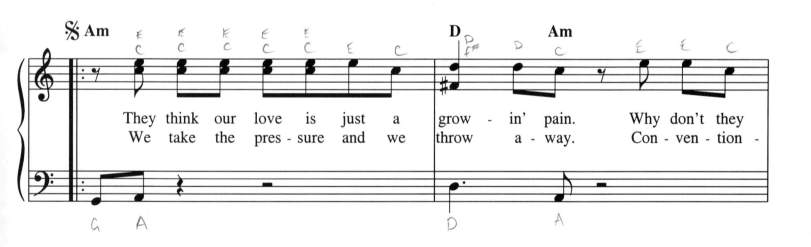

They think our love is just a grow - in' pain. Why don't they
We take the pres - sure and we throw a - way. Con - ven - tion -

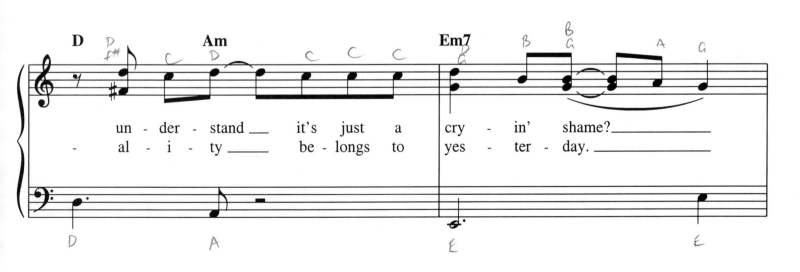

un - der - stand ____ it's just a cry - in' shame? _____
- al - i - ty ____ be - longs to yes - ter - day. _____

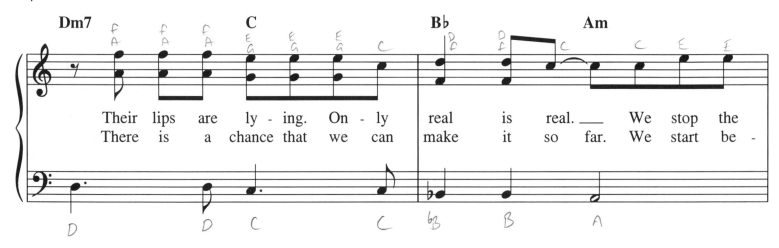

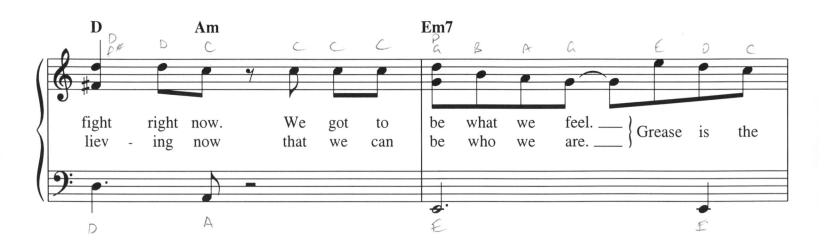

HOPELESSLY DEVOTED TO YOU

Words and Music by
JOHN FARRAR

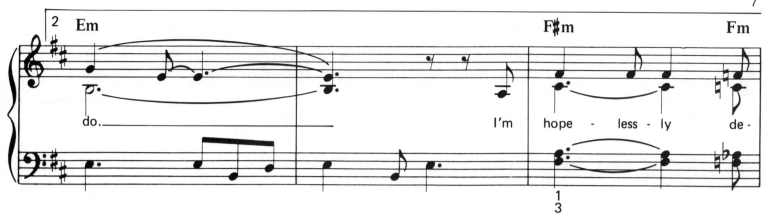

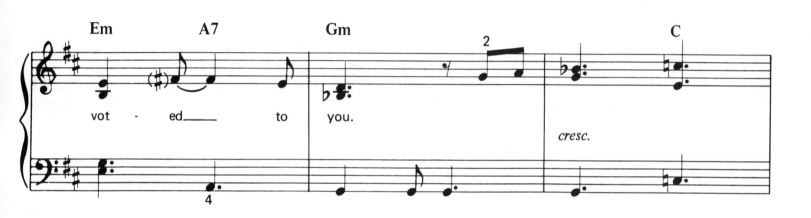

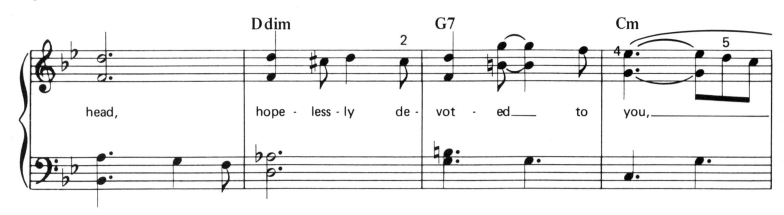

head, hope - less - ly de - vot - ed___ to you,___

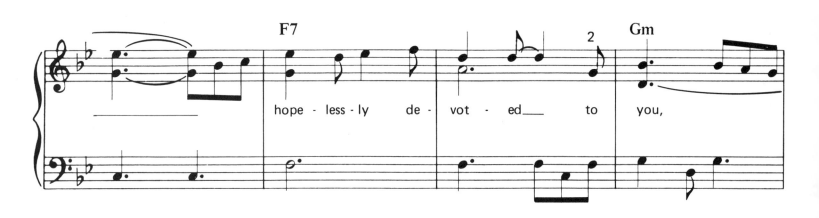

___ hope - less - ly de - vot - ed___ to you,

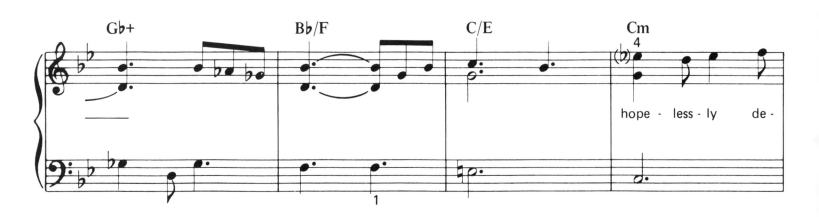

___ hope - less - ly de -

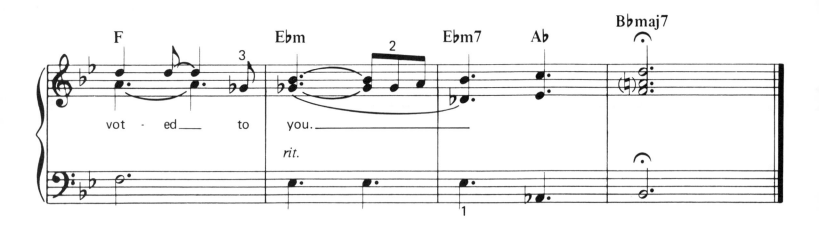

vot - ed___ to you.___

rit.

YOU'RE THE ONE THAT I WANT

Words and Music by
JOHN FARRAR

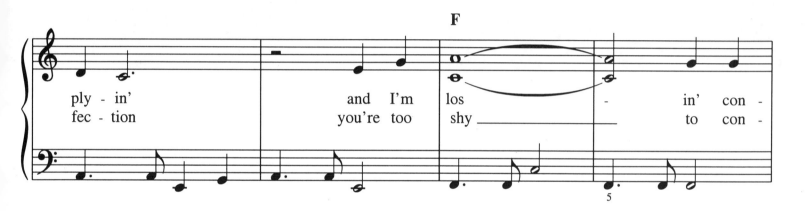

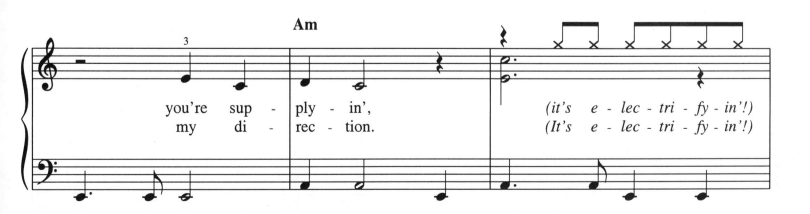

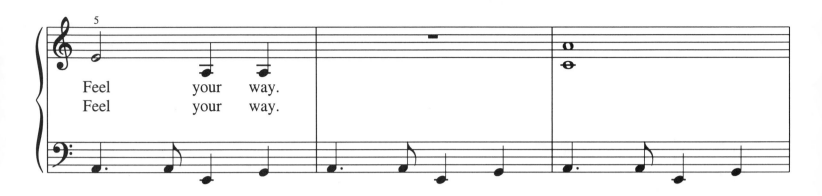

Feel your way.
Feel your way.

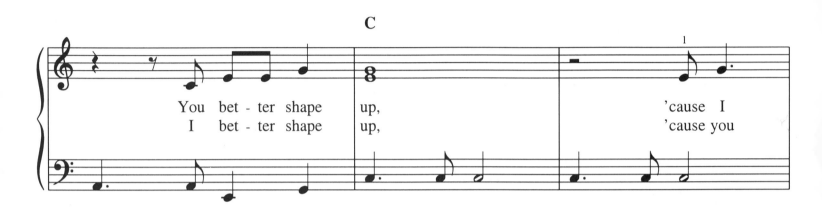

C

You bet - ter shape up, 'cause I
I bet - ter shape up, 'cause you

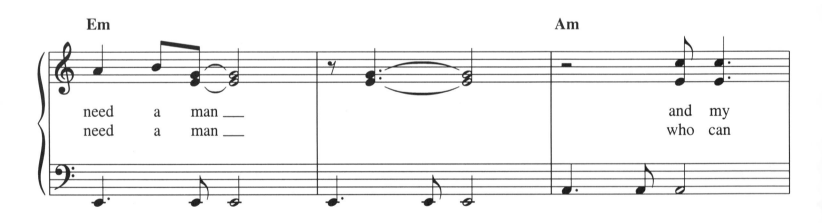

Em   **Am**

need a man ___ and my
need a man ___ who can

F

heart is set on you.
keep you sat - is - fied.

You bet - ter shape
I bet - ter shape

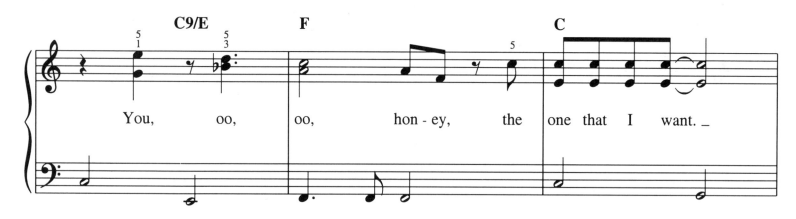

You, oo, oo, hon - ey, the one that I want. _

You, oo, oo hon - ey, the

one that I want. _ You, oo,

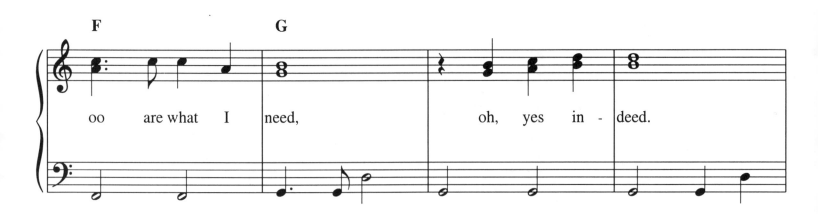

oo are what I need, oh, yes in - deed.

13

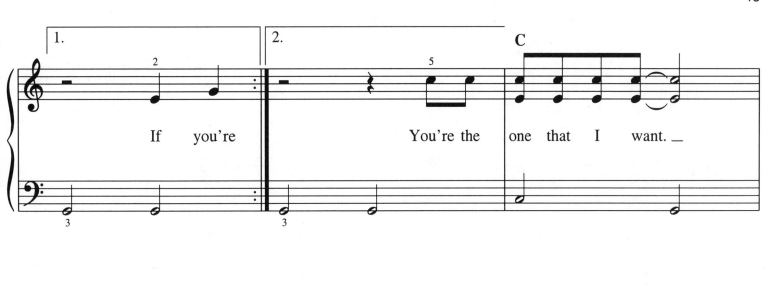

SANDY

Words and Music by SCOTT SIMON
and LOUIS ST. LOUIS

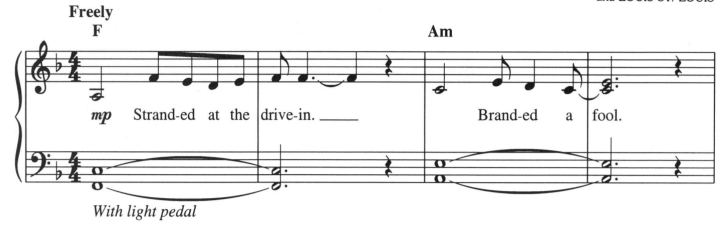

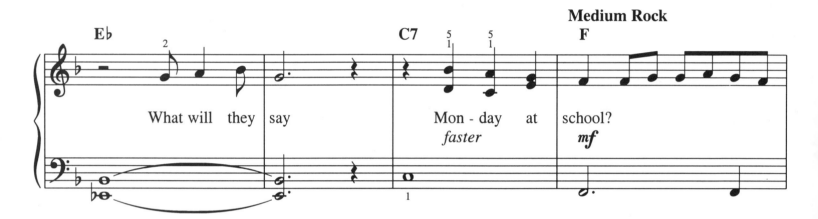

C7 / Gm7 / C7

y? We made a start. _ Now we're a-part. _ There's

B♭/F / B♭m/F / F / E♭/F / F7

noth-in' left for me. Love has flown. _

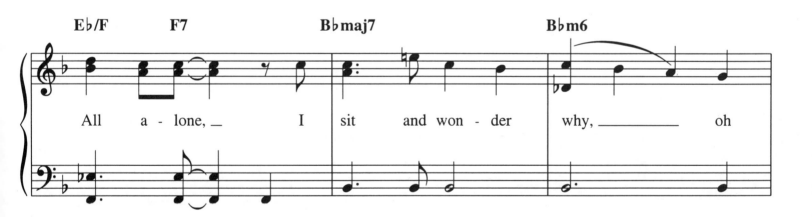

E♭/F / F7 / B♭maj7 / B♭m6

All a-lone, _ I sit and won-der why, _____ oh

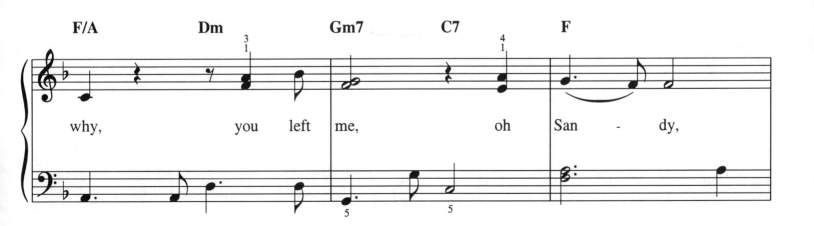

F/A / Dm / Gm7 / C7 / F

why, you left me, oh San - dy,

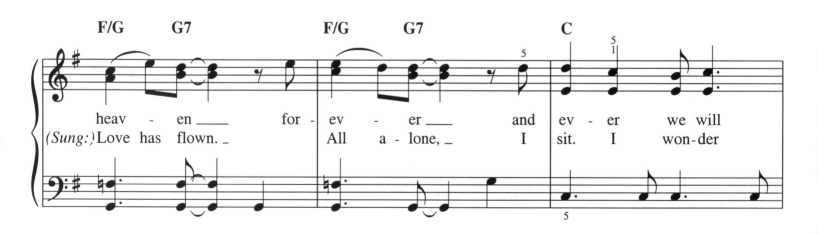

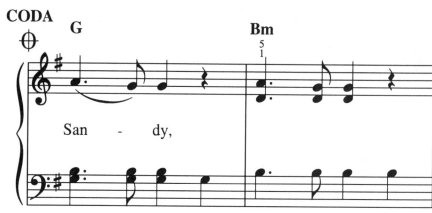

BEAUTY SCHOOL DROPOUT

Lyric and Music by WARREN CASEY
and JIM JACOBS

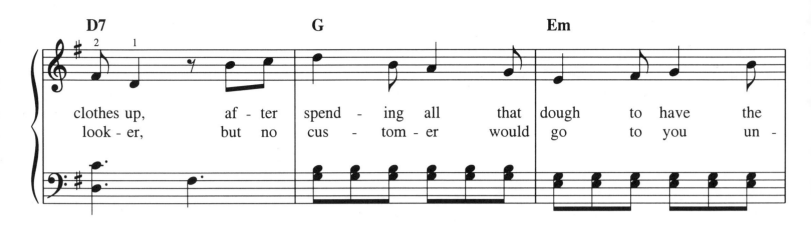

clothes up, af - ter spend - ing all that dough to have the
look - er, but no cus - tom - er would go to you un -

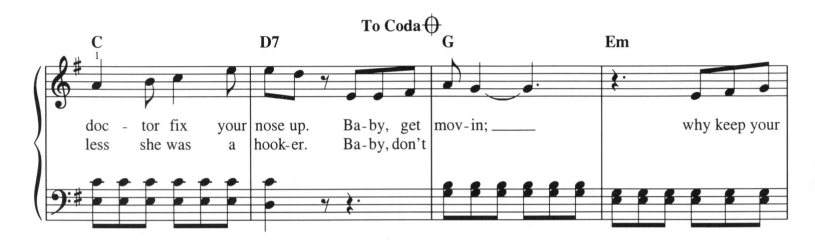

To Coda ⊕

doc - tor fix your nose up. Ba - by, get mov - in; _____ why keep your
less she was a hook - er. Ba - by, don't

fee - ble hopes a - live?_____ What are you prov - in? _____ You got the

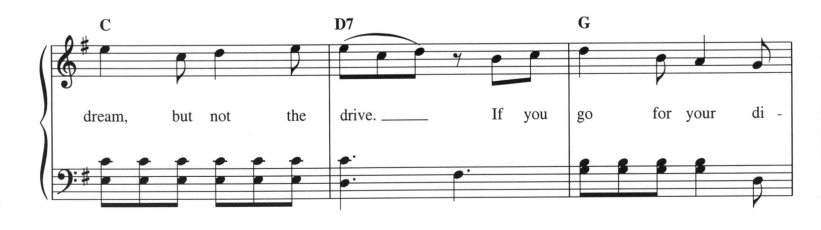

dream, but not the drive. _____ If you go for your di -

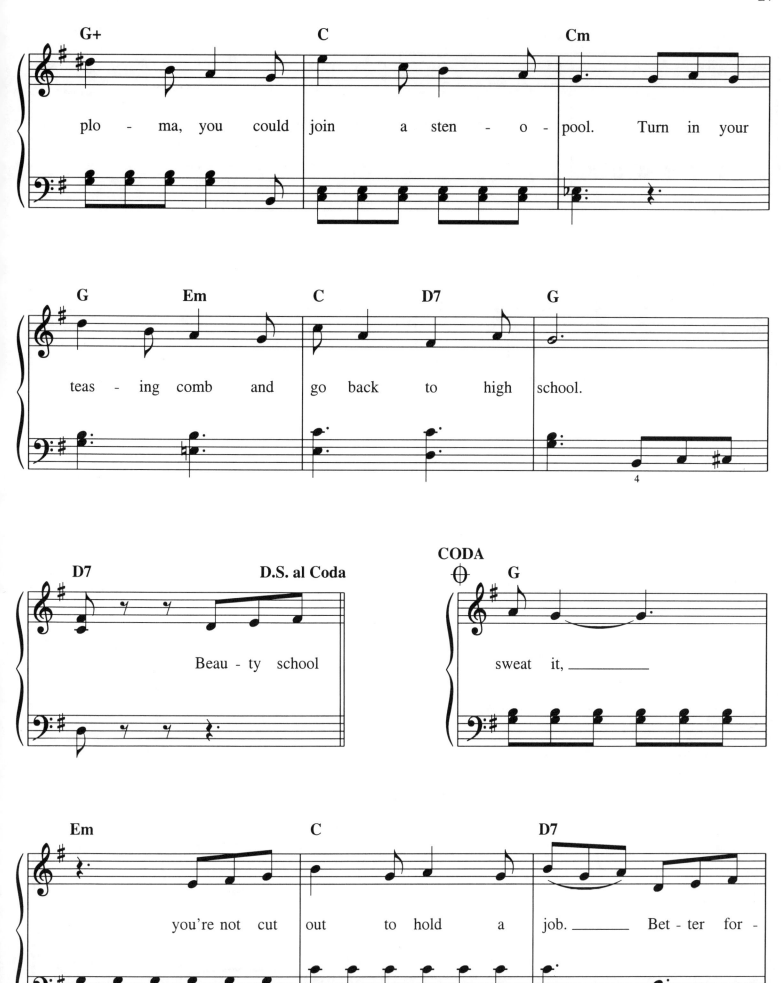

get it; _____ who wants their hair done by a slob? ___ Now, your

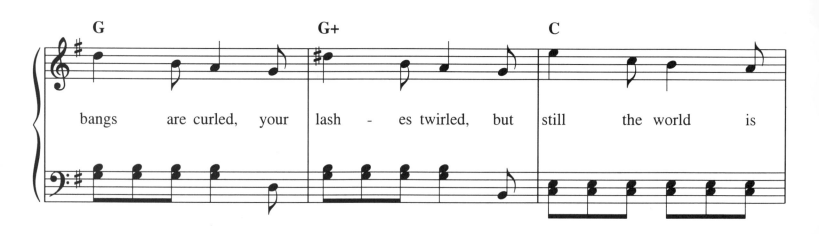

bangs are curled, your lash - es twirled, but still the world is

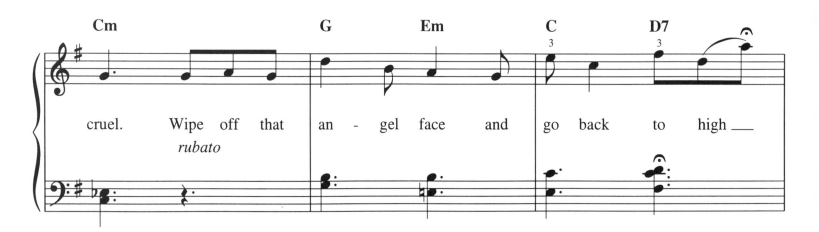

cruel. Wipe off that an - gel face and go back to high ___
rubato

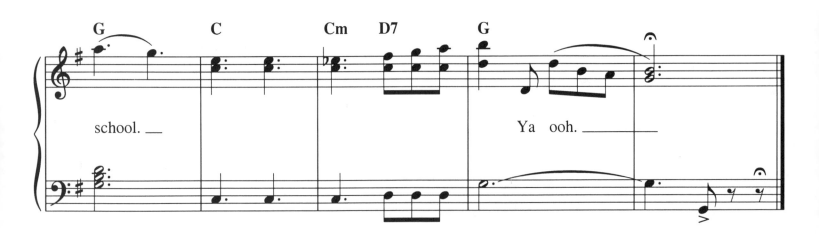

school. __ Ya ooh. _____

LOOK AT ME, I'M SANDRA DEE

Fast Rinky Dink Waltz in 1

Lyric and Music by WARREN CASEY
and JIM JACOBS

24

SUMMER NIGHTS

Lyric and Music by WARREN CASEY
and JIM JACOBS

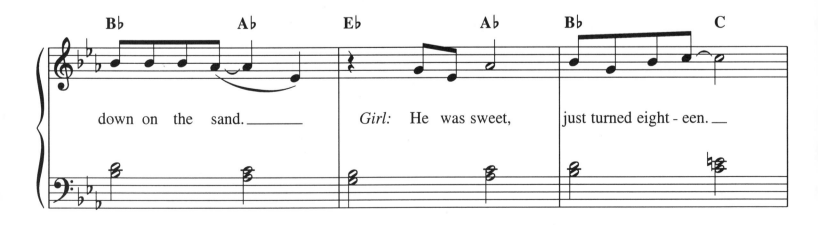

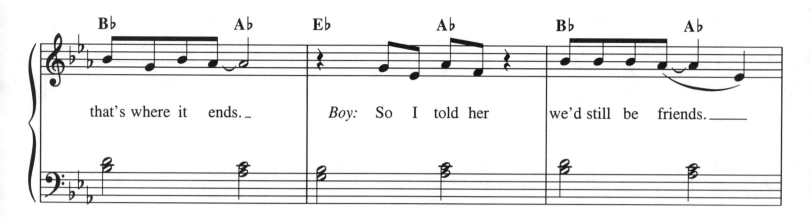

that's where it ends.＿ *Boy:* So I told her we'd still be friends.＿＿

Girl: Then we made our true love vow.＿ *Boy:* Won-der what

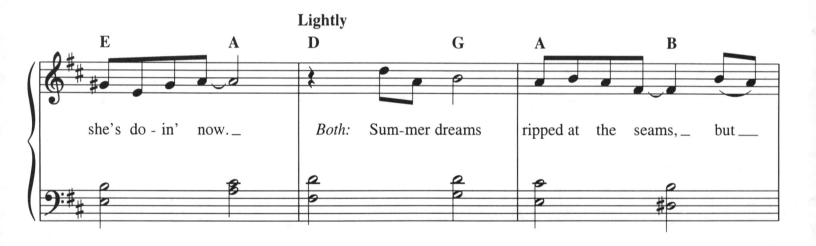

Lightly

she's do-in' now.＿ *Both:* Sum-mer dreams ripped at the seams,＿ but＿

oh, those sum-mer nights.＿ *Chorus:* Tell me more, tell me more.

GREASED LIGHTNIN'

Lyric and Music by WARREN CASEY
and JIM JACOBS

Hard driving Rock and Roll

I'll have me o-ver-head lift-ers and
pur-ple French tail-lights and

four bar-rel quads, oh, yeah. Ah,
thir - ty inch fins, oh, yeah. Ah,

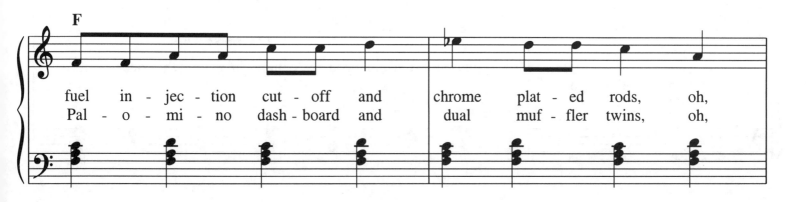

fuel in - jec - tion cut - off and chrome plat - ed rods, oh,
Pal - o - mi - no dash - board and dual muf - fler twins, oh,

yeah. With a four-speed on the floor they'll be
yeah. With new pis - tons, plugs and shocks, she could

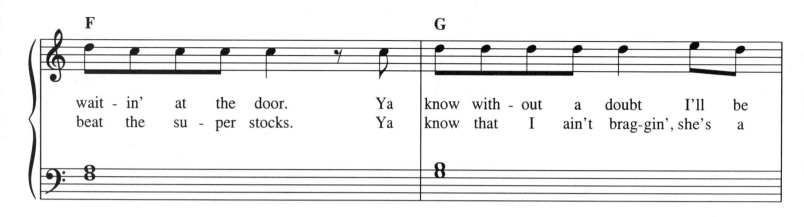

wait - in' at the door. Ya know with - out a doubt I'll be
beat the su - per stocks. Ya know that I ain't brag - gin', she's a

real - ly mak - in' out in Greased Light - nin'.
real ___ drag - on wag - on, my Greased Light - nin'.
(Go, go, go,

go, go, go, go.) Go, Greased Light-nin', you're burn- in' up the quar - ter

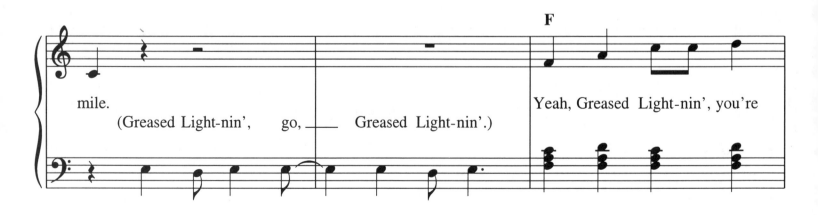

mile.
(Greased Light-nin', go, ___ Greased Light-nin'.)
Yeah, Greased Light-nin', you're

IT'S RAINING ON PROM NIGHT

Lyric and Music by WARREN CASEY
and JIM JACOBS

Slow and dreamy (Cha-Cha)

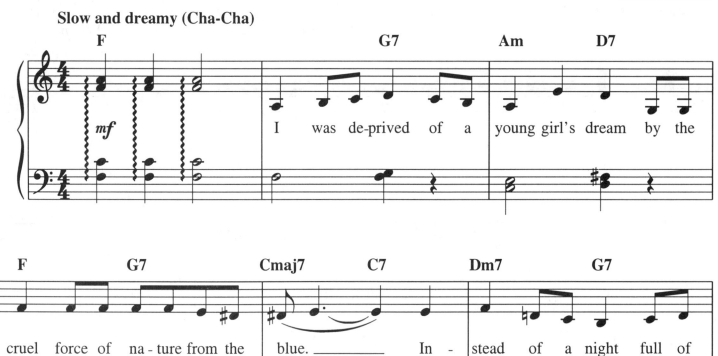

I was de-prived of a young girl's dream by the cruel force of na-ture from the blue. _____ In - stead of a night full of ro - mance su -preme, all I got was a run - ny nose and A - si - at - ic flu. It's

rain - ing _____ on prom night, _____ my hair is a

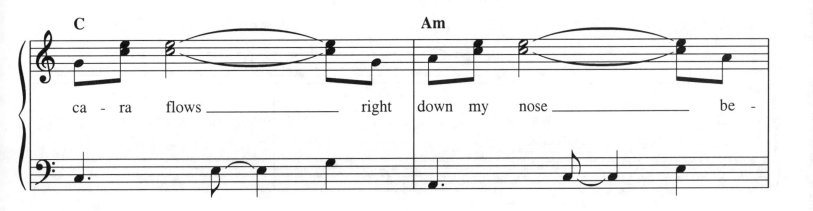

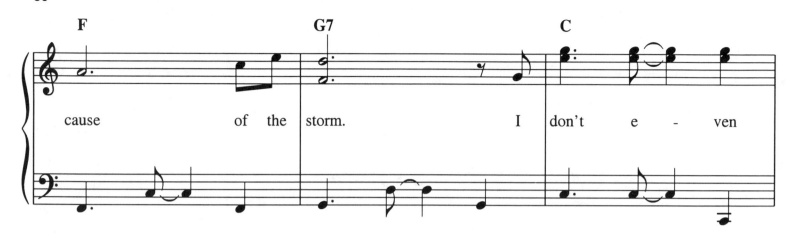

cause   of the storm.   I don't e - ven

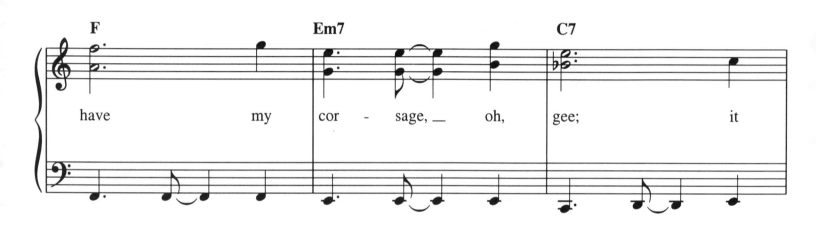

have   my cor - sage, __ oh, gee;   it

fell down __ a sew - er __ with my sis - ter's __ I.

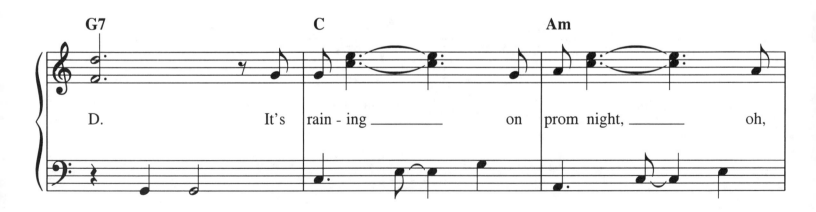

D.   It's rain - ing _____ on prom night, _____ oh,

what can I do? It's rain - ing ___

rain from the skies, ___ it's rain - ing ___

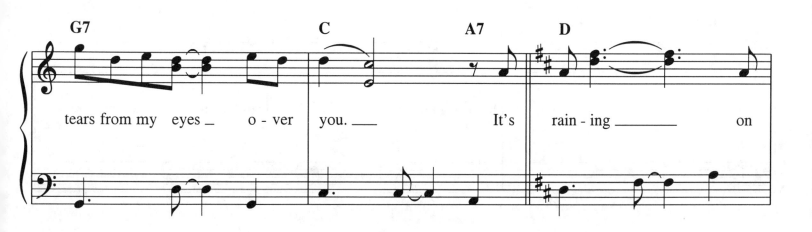

tears from my eyes ___ o - ver you. ___ It's rain - ing ___ on

prom night, ___ oh, what can I

BLUE MOON

Words by LORENZ HART
Music by RICHARD RODGERS

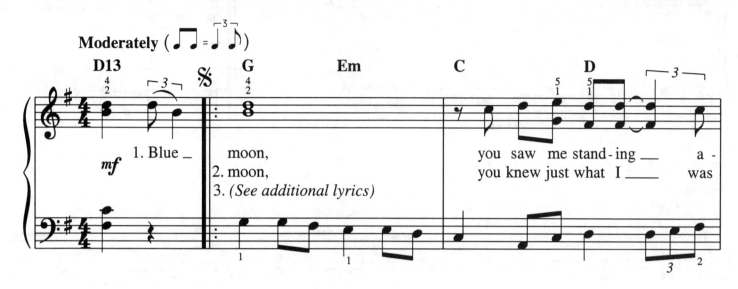

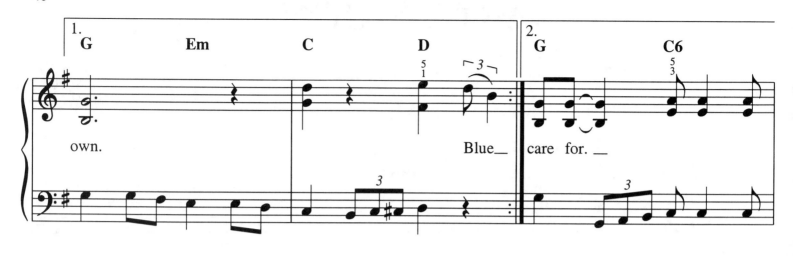

own.　　　　　　　　　　　　　　Blue___ care for. ___

And then sud - den - ly _____ ap -

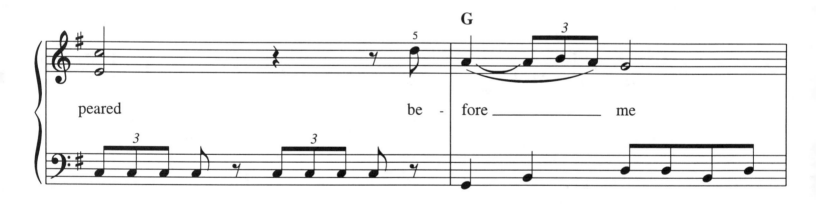

peared　　　　　　　　　　　　be - fore _____ me

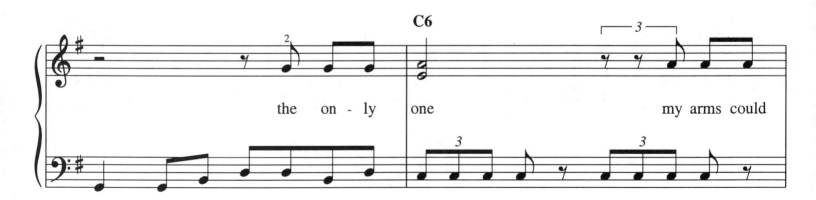

the on - ly one　　　　　　　　　　my arms could

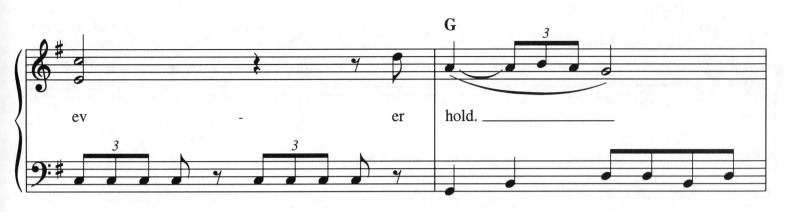

ev - - - er hold. _____

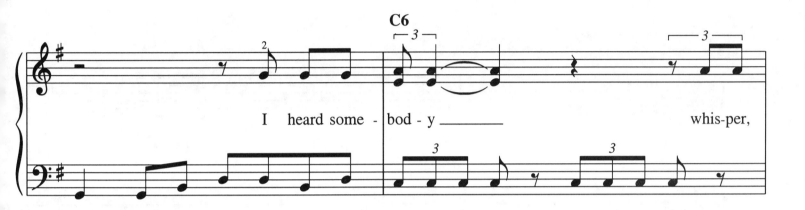

I heard some - bod - y _____ whis-per,

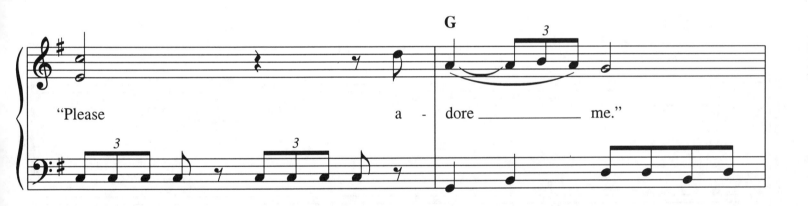

"Please a - dore _____ me."

But when I looked, that moon had turned to

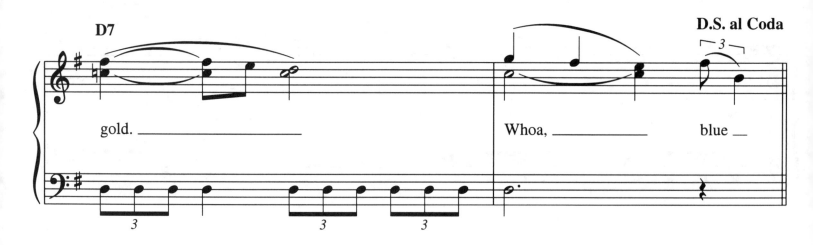

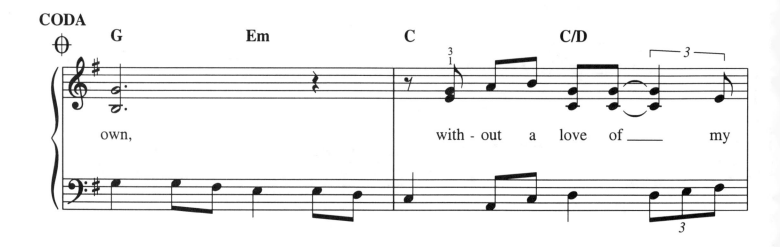

Additional Lyrics

3. Whoa, blue moon, now I'm no longer alone,
   Without a dream in my heart,
   Without a love of my own,
   Without a love of my own.

MOONING

Lyric and Music by WARREN CASEY
and JIM JACOBS

ing all o - ver you. _____ (All o - ver

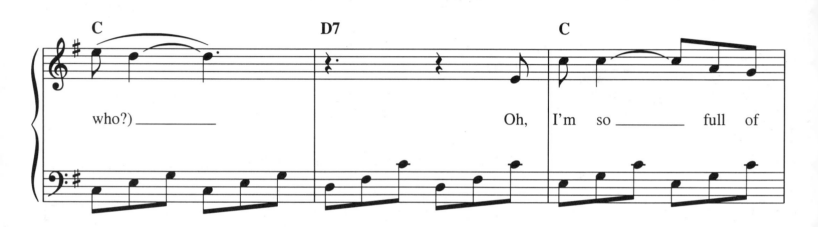

who?) _____ Oh, I'm so _____ full of

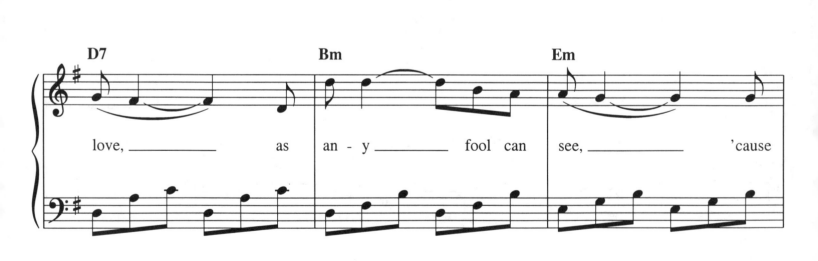

love, _____ as an - y _____ fool can see, _____ 'cause

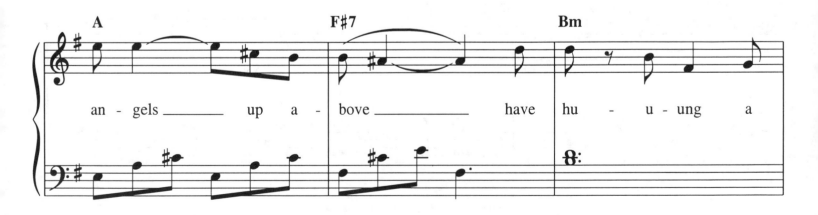

an - gels _____ up a - bove _____ have hu - u - ung a

ing   if you would call me _____   (up on the

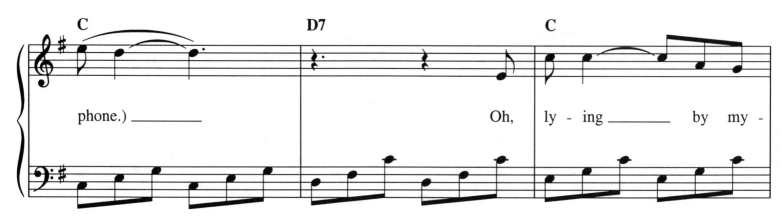

phone.) _____   Oh, ly - ing _____ by my -

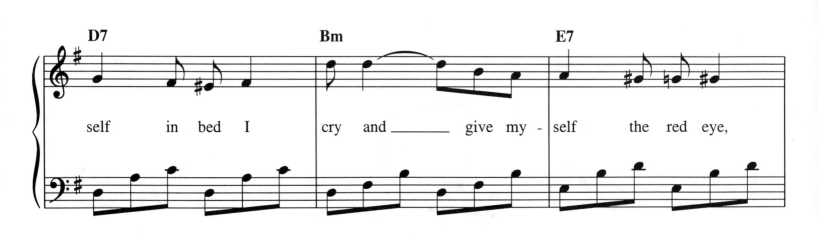

self   in bed I   cry and _____ give my - self   the red eye,

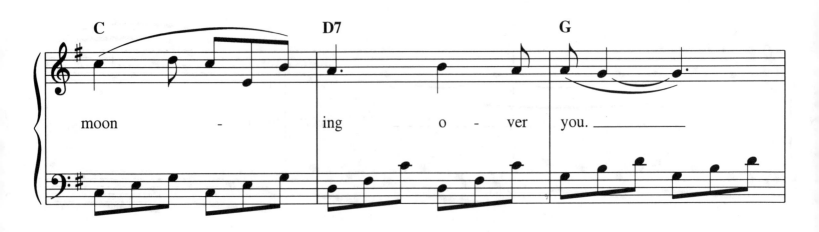

moon   -   ing   o - ver you. _____

ALONE AT THE DRIVE-IN MOVIE

Lyric and Music by WARREN CASEY
and JIM JACOBS

Melancholy, slow ballad

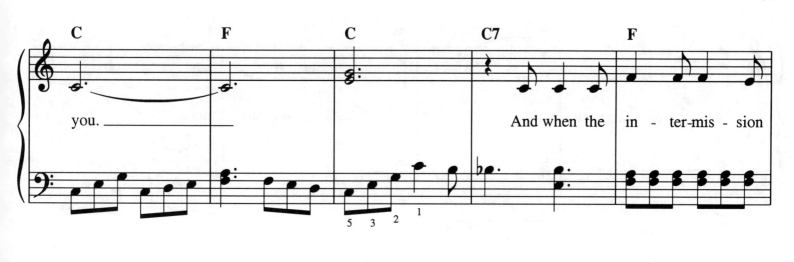

you. _____ And when the in - ter-mis - sion

elf _____ moves the clock's hands, _____ when he's eat - ing _____ ev - 'ry -

thing sold at the stand, when there's one min-ute to

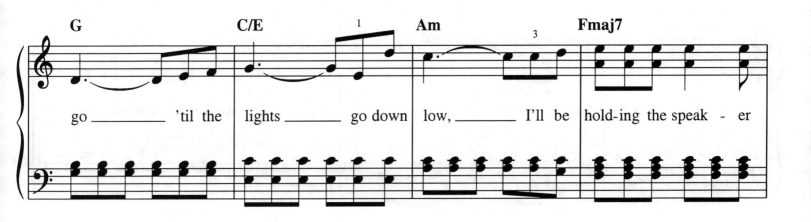

go _____ 'til the lights _____ go down low, _____ I'll be hold-ing the speak - er

ROCK AND ROLL IS HERE TO STAY

Words and Music by
DAVID WHITE

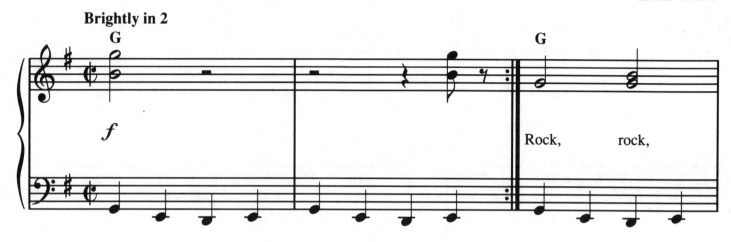

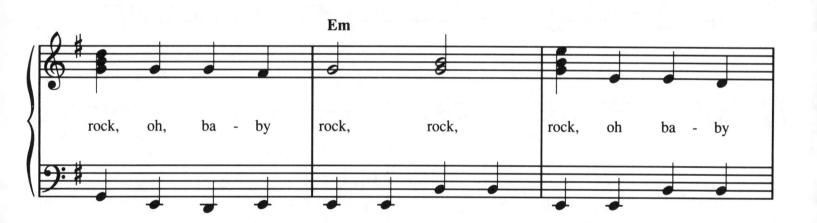

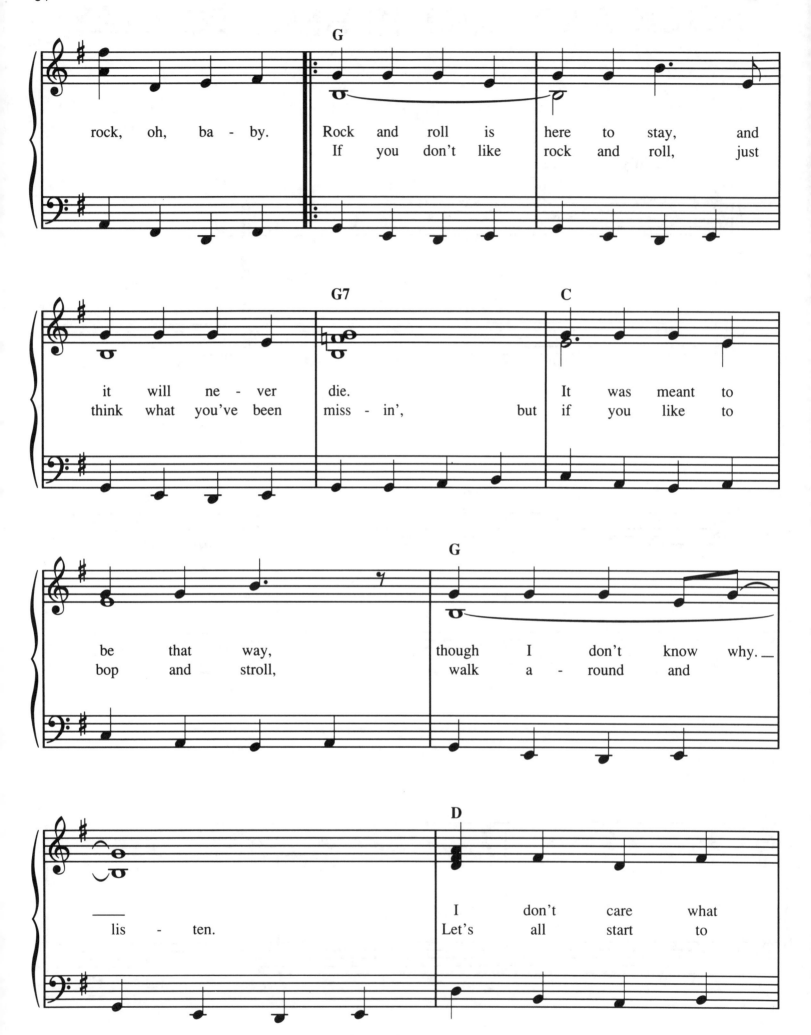

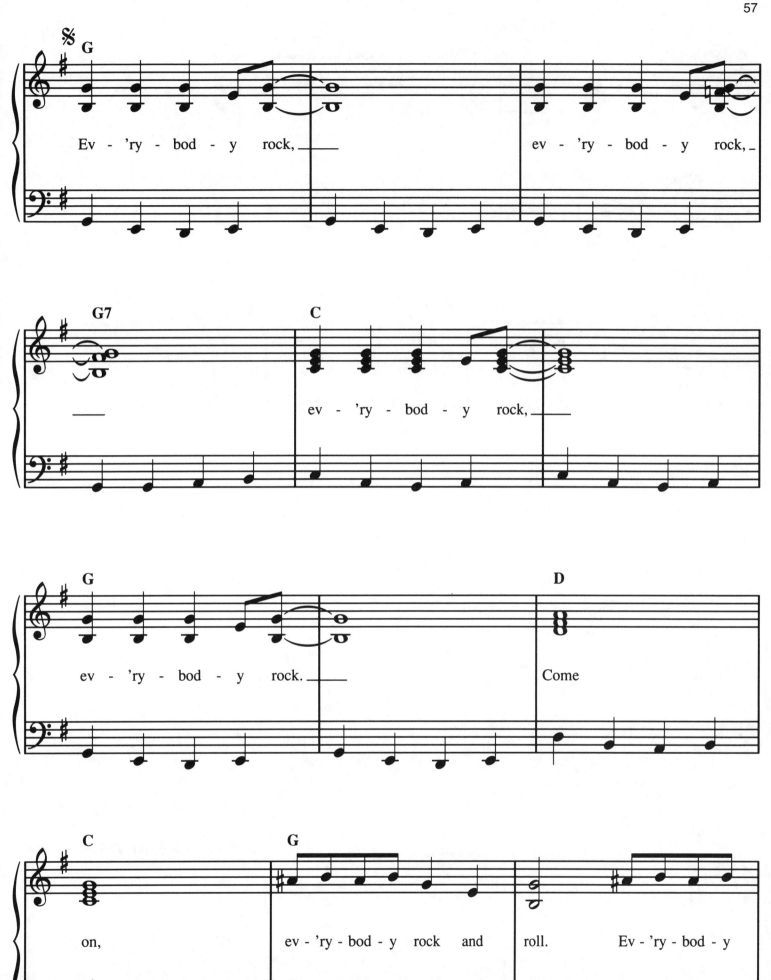

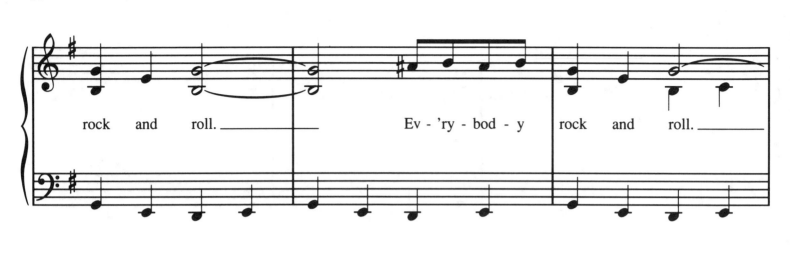

rock and roll. _____ Ev - 'ry - bod - y rock and roll. _____

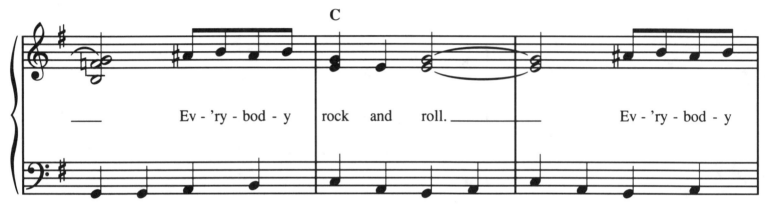

_____ Ev - 'ry - bod - y rock and roll. _____ Ev - 'ry - bod - y

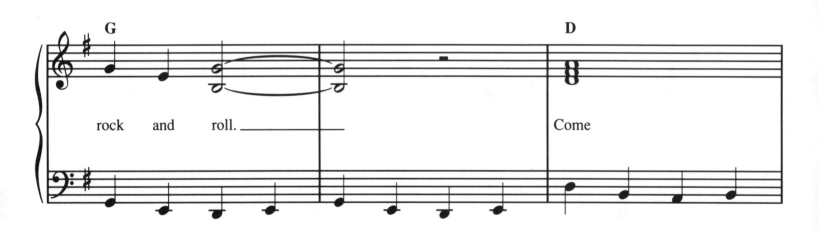

rock and roll. _____ Come

2nd time D.S. and Fade

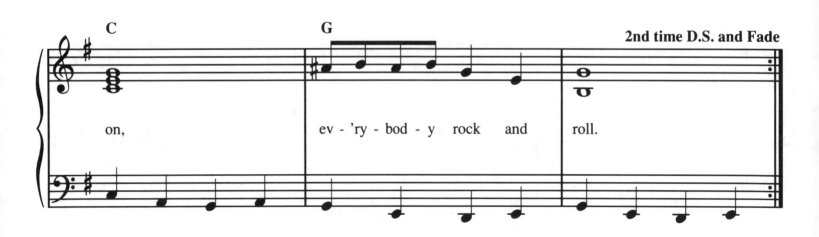

on, ev - 'ry - bod - y rock and roll.

THOSE MAGIC CHANGES

Lyric and Music by WARREN CASEY
and JIM JACOBS

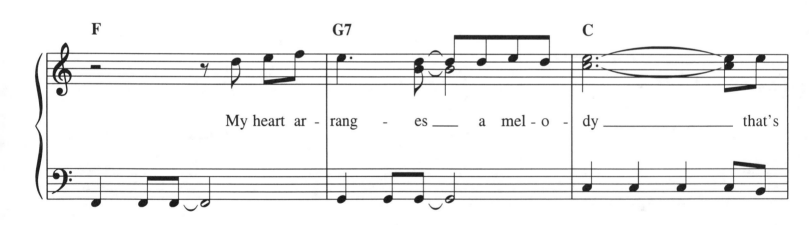

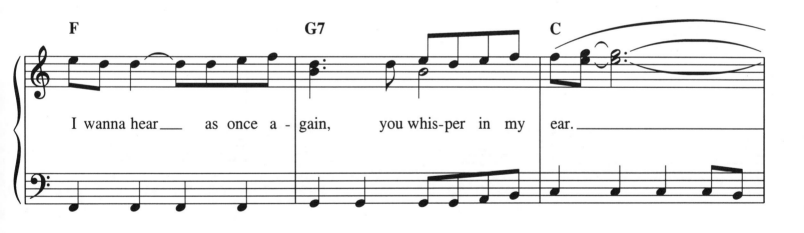

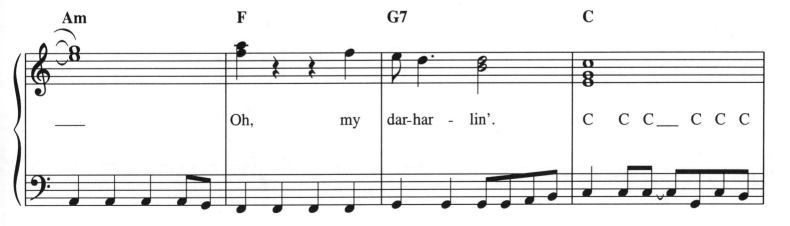

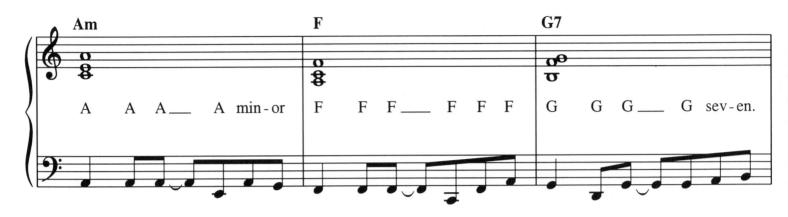

A A A__ A min-or F F F__ F F F G G G__ G sev-en.

I'll be wait - ing by the ra - di - o, ___ you'll come back_ to me some-

day, I know._ Been so lone - some since your last good-bye, _

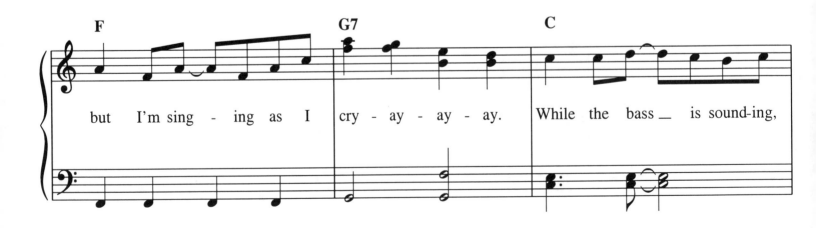

but I'm sing - ing as I cry - ay - ay - ay. While the bass _ is sound-ing,

HOUND DOG

Words and Music by JERRY LEIBER
and MIKE STOLLER

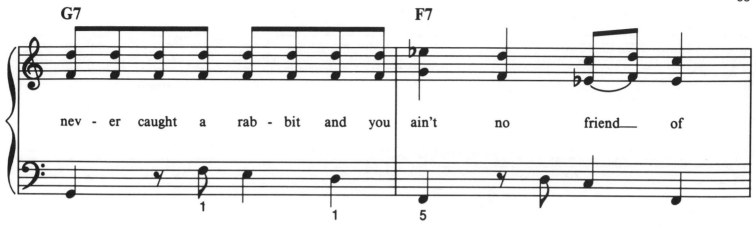

nev - er caught a rab - bit and you ain't no friend_ of

mine. When they said you was high - classed,

well, that was just a lie. When they said you was

high - classed, well, that was just a

BORN TO HAND JIVE

Lyric and Music by WARREN CASEY
and JIM JACOBS

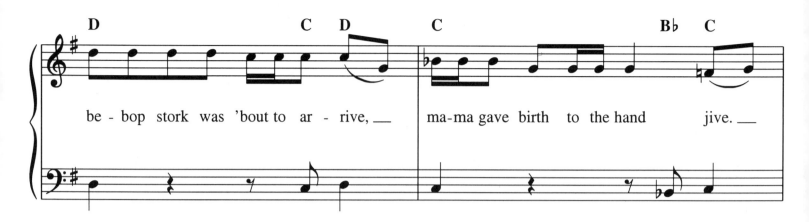

be - bop stork was 'bout to ar - rive, ___ ma-ma gave birth to the hand jive. ___

I could bare-ly walk when I milked a cow, _

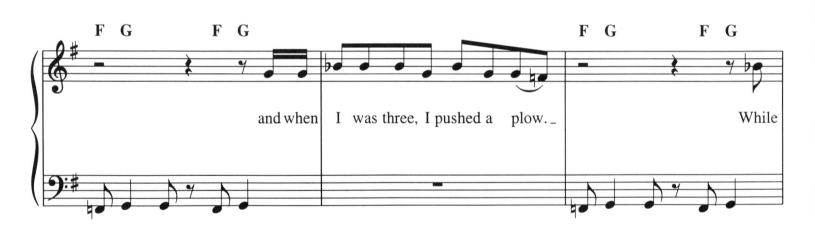

and when I was three, I pushed a plow. _ While

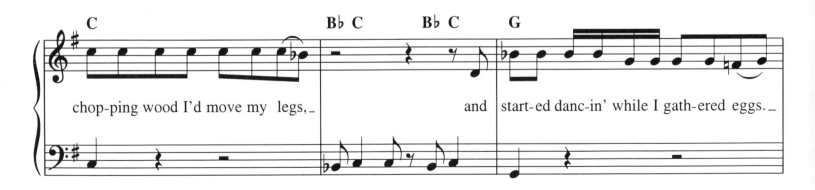

chop-ping wood I'd move my legs, _ and start-ed danc-in' while I gath-ered eggs. _

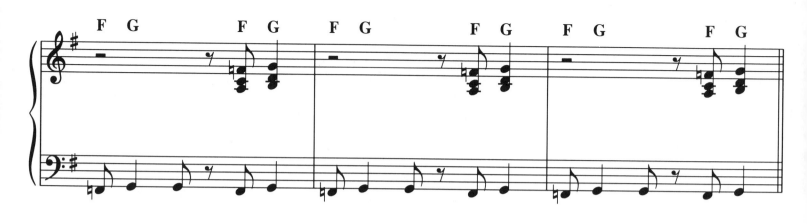

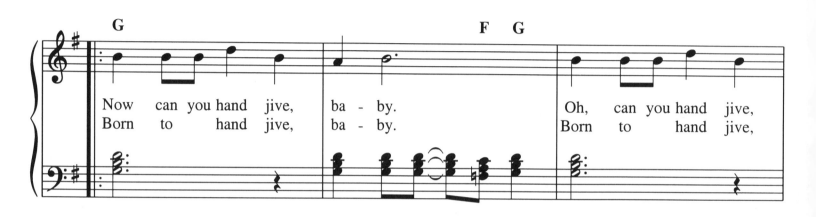

Now can you hand jive, ba - by. Oh, can you hand jive,
Born to hand jive, ba - by. Born to hand jive,

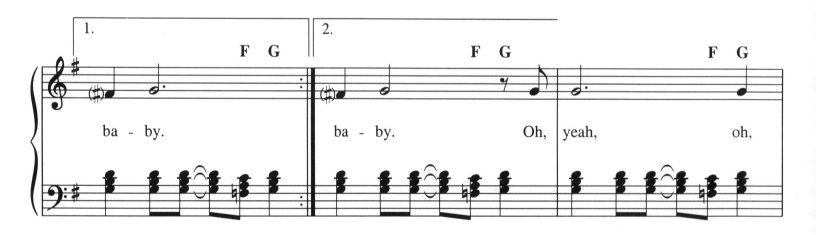

ba - by.
ba - by. Oh, yeah, oh,

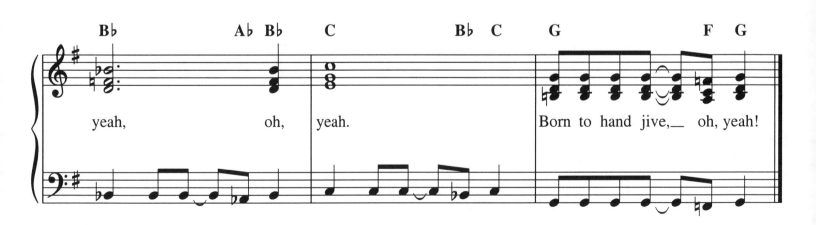

yeah, oh, yeah. Born to hand jive,__ oh, yeah!

TEARS ON MY PILLOW

Words and Music by SYLVESTER BRADFORD
and AL LEWIS

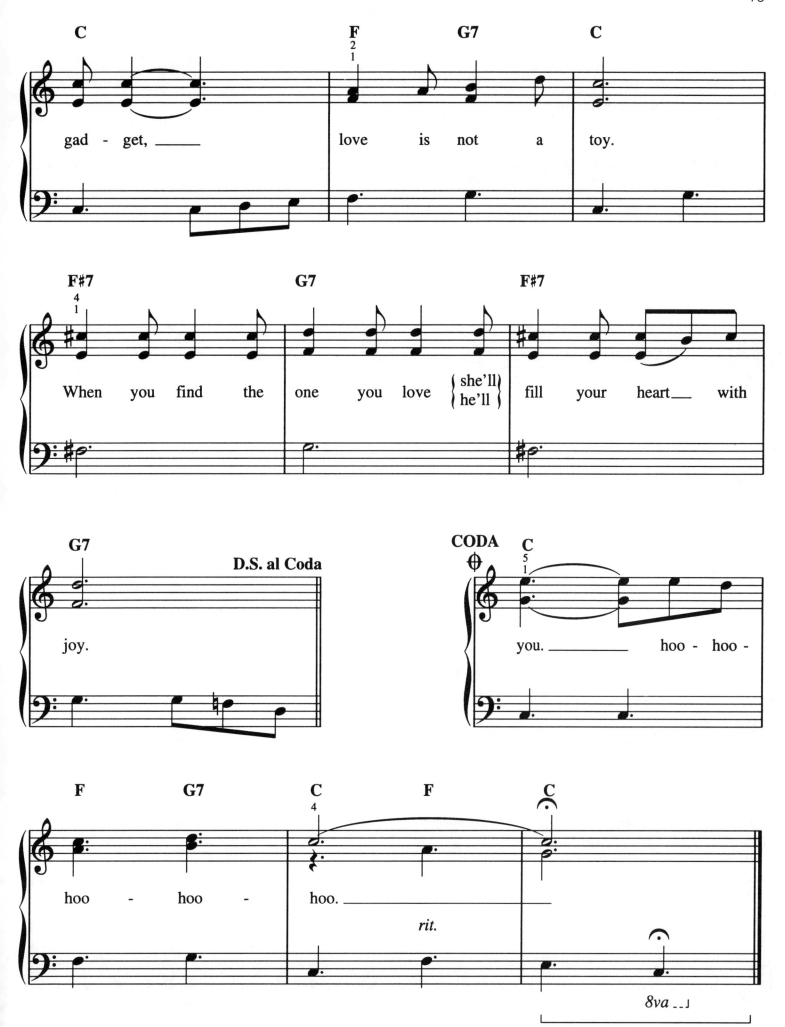

FREDDY, MY LOVE

Lyric and Music by WARREN CASEY
and JIM JACOBS

Fred-dy, my love, I miss you more than __ words can say.
know, your ab-sence makes me __ feel so blue.
see, you'll hold me in your __ arms some-day.

Fred-dy, my love, please keep in touch while __ you're a-way.
That's o-kay, though, your pres-ents make me __ think of you.
And I will be wear-ing your lac-y __ lin-ge-rie.

Hear-ing from you can make the day __ so much bet-ter,
Ma-ma will have a heart at-tack __ when she catch-es
Think-ing a-bout it my heart's pound-ing al-read-y,

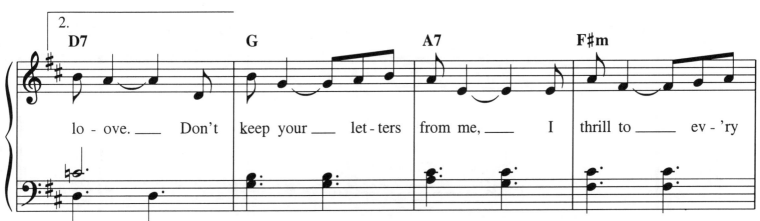

line. Your spell-ing's — kind-a crum-my, — but, hon-ey, — so is mine. I

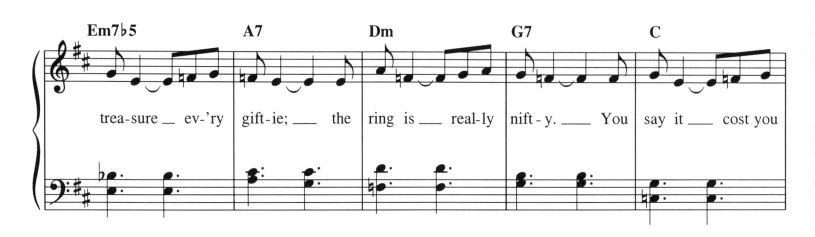

trea-sure — ev-'ry gift-ie; — the ring is — real-ly nift-y. — You say it — cost you

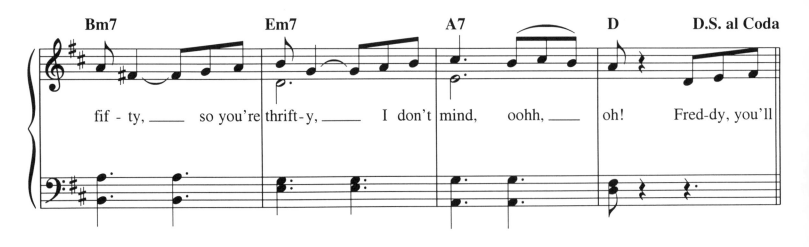

fif - ty, — so you're thrift-y, — I don't mind, oohh, — oh! Fred-dy, you'll

love, Fred-dy, my love, Fred-dy, my lo-ove. Fred-dy, my love.

ROCK 'N' ROLL PARTY QUEEN

Lyric and Music by WARREN CASEY
and JIM JACOBS

Lit-tle girl, ya know who I mean, — pret-ty soon she'll be sev-en-teen. —

They tell — me her name's Bet-ty Jean, — the, ha, ha, rock 'n' roll pa-ar-ty queen.

Fri-day night and she's got a date, —
She's the girl that all the kids know, —

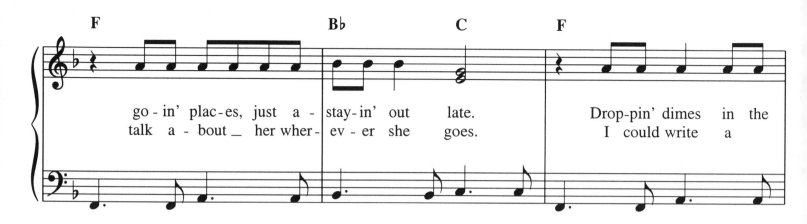

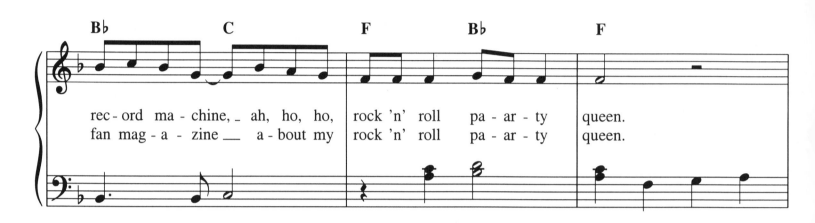

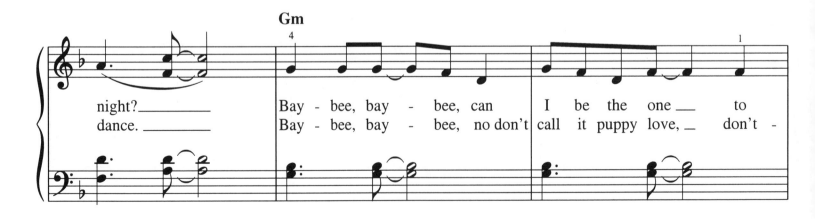

love you with all ____ of my mi - hite?
cha wan - na tru - hu ro - ma - hance?
Ay, yi, yi, yi.

Rock-in' and a roll-in' lit-tle par - ty queen, _ we gon-na do the stroll, you' my

par - ty queen. _ Ya know I love you so, hey, par - ty queen, _ you're my

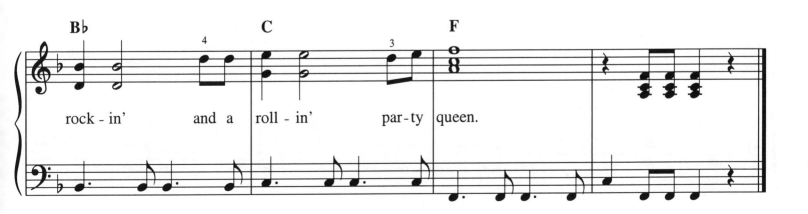

rock - in' and a roll - in' par - ty queen.

THERE ARE WORSE THINGS I COULD DO

Lyric and Music by WARREN CASEY
and JIM JACOBS

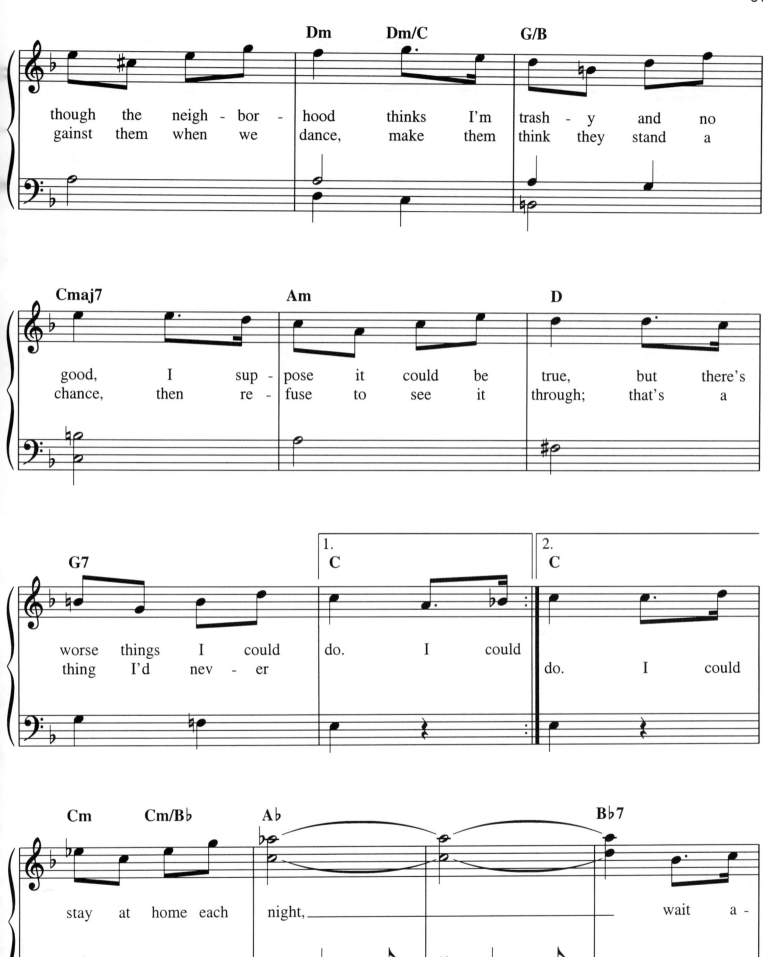

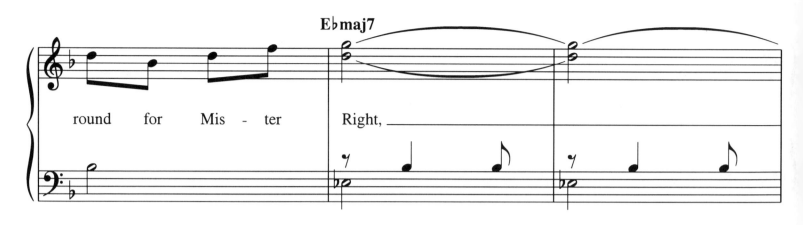

round for Mis - ter Right, _____

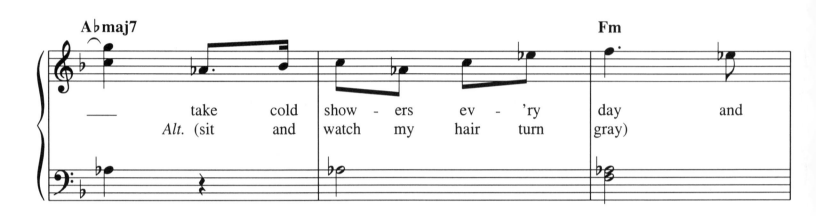

_____ take cold show - ers ev - 'ry day and
Alt. (sit and watch my hair turn gray)

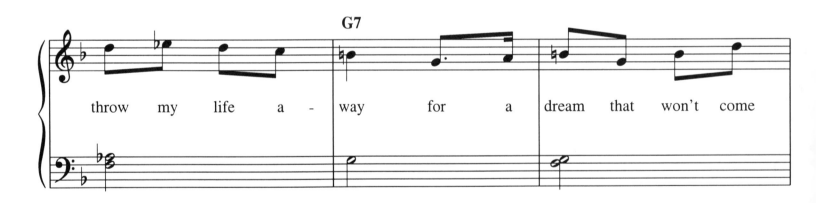

throw my life a - way for a dream that won't come

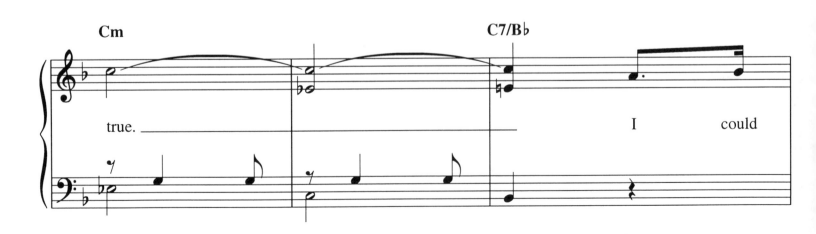

true. _____ I could

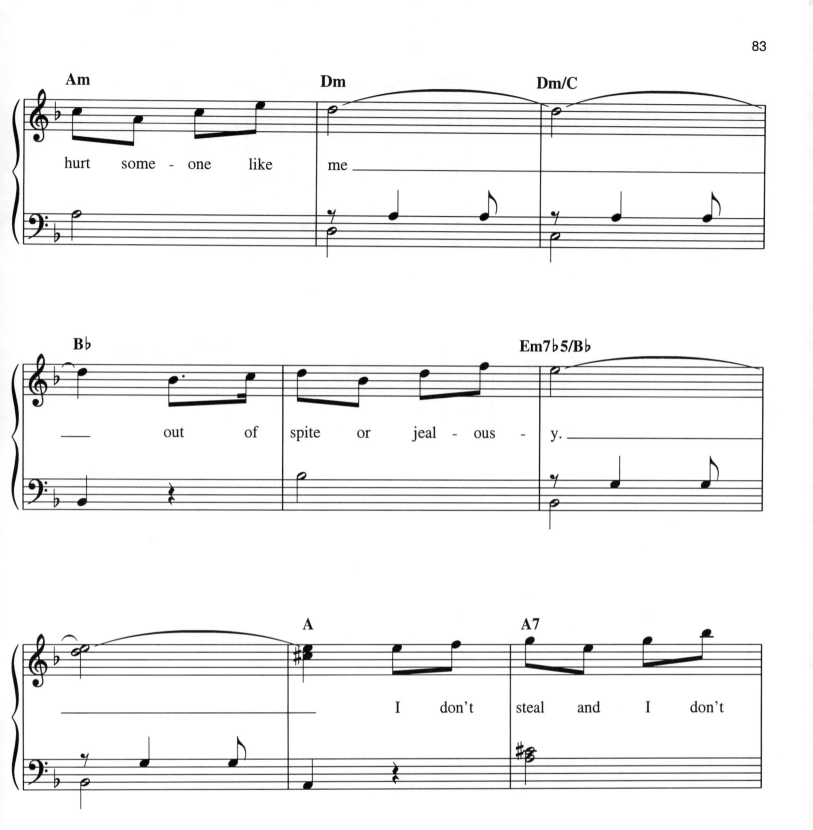

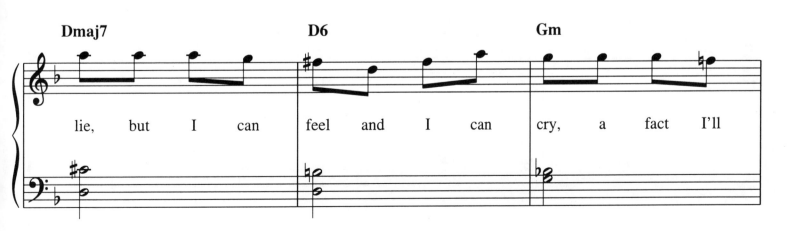

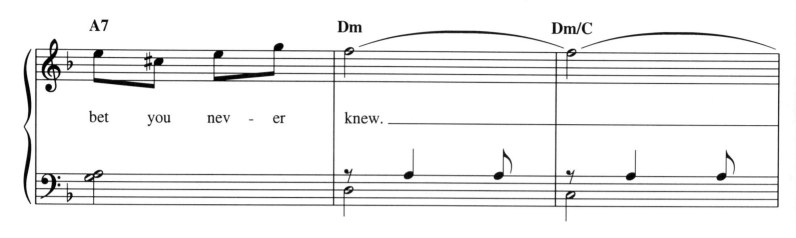

bet you nev - er knew. _____

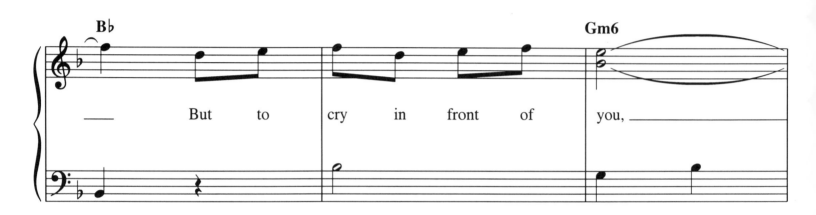

_____ But to cry in front of you, _____

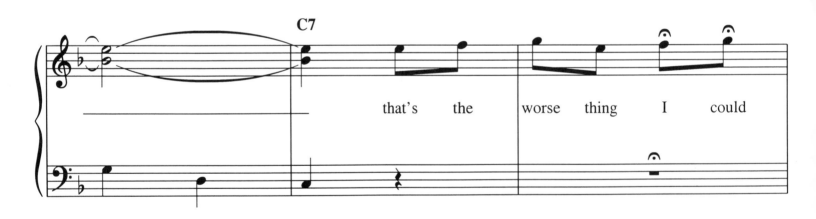

_____ that's the worse thing I could

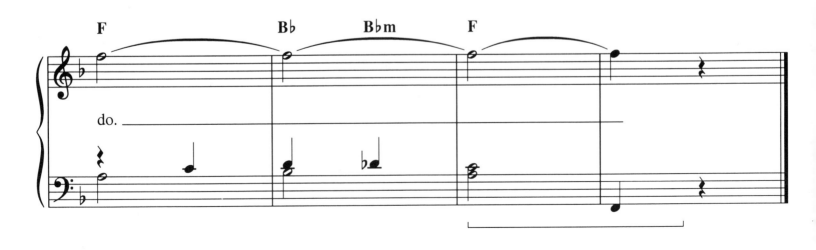

do. _____

WE GO TOGETHER

Lyric and Music by WARREN CASEY
and JIM JACOBS

Moderate Rock in 2

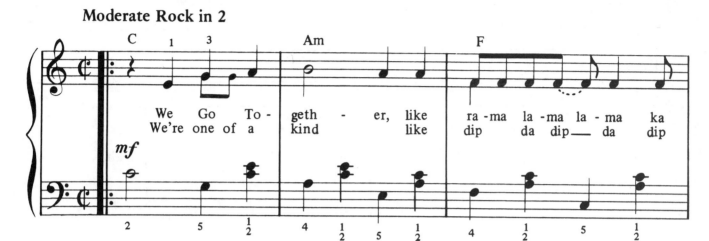

We Go To - geth - er, like ra - ma la - ma la - ma ka
We're one of a kind like dip da dip __ da dip

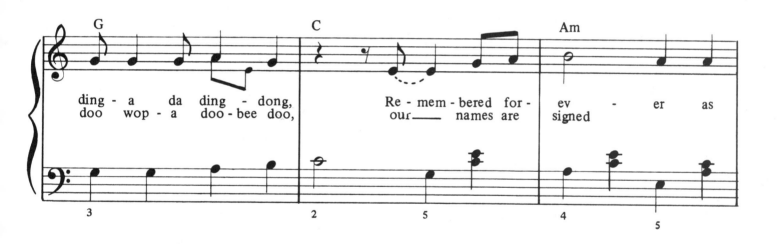

ding - a da ding - dong, Re - mem - bered for - ev - er as
doo wop - a doo - bee doo, our __ names are signed

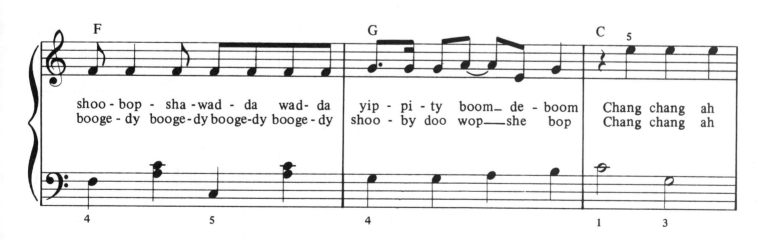

shoo - bop - sha - wad - da wad - da yip - pi - ty boom __ de - boom Chang chang ah
booge - dy booge - dy booge - dy booge - dy shoo - by doo wop __ she bop Chang chang ah